Science Stories of Ancient China

Distinguished Doctors of Ancient China

Written by Zhu Kang

Illustrated by Hong Tao and Feng Congying

Bian Que's Four Methods of Diagnosis
Hua Tuo's *Mafeisan* **and Five-Animal Exercises**
Wang Weiyi's Bronze Figure Inscribed with
    the Acupoints
Compendium of Materia Medica **by Li Shizhen**

⑤ DOLPHIN BOOKS

图书在版编目（CIP）数据

中国古代医学家 / 朱抗编写; 洪涛, 冯聪英绘.
北京: 海豚出版社, 2005. 7
(中国古代科学故事丛书)
ISBN 7-80138-498-9

I. 中...   II. ①朱... ②洪... ③冯...
III. 医学家－列传－中国－古代－英文
IV. K826. 2

中国版本图书馆CIP数据核字（2005）第080643号

First Edition 2005

ISBN 7-80138-498-9

© Dolphin Books, Beijing, 2005

Published by Dolphin Books
24 Baiwanzhuang Road, Beijing 100037, China

Distributed by China International Book Trading
Corporation
35 Chegongzhuang Xilu, Beijing 100044, China
P.O.Box 399, Beijing, China

Printed in the People's Republic of China

Bian Que

Bian Que, originally named Qin Yueren (401-314 B.C.), was one of the founders of traditional Chinese medicine. It was he who first used and systematized traditional Chinese medical ways into the Four Methods of Diagnosis; that is, to observe, to smell, to ask and to feel.

At that time, people attached more importance to ghosts and gods than to doctors. Whenever fatal epidemic diseases occurred, grand-scale ceremonies for getting rid of them were held and people prayed to the gods for soundness and safety.

Qin Yueren did odd jobs at an inn when he was young.

Why do you stare blankly? Go and do your jobs quickly.

Those wizards have been trying to get rid of ghosts for more than ten days, but more and more people die.

Why can't the gods of plague be dispelled?

Alas!

Leave here quickly! If others are infected with the disease, my business will stop.

I feel weak all over and can't walk any more.

He has no one to turn to for help. Where should he go?

Wait a minute, please. Let me have a look.

This is an old folk doctor named Chang-sang.

Decoct doses of medicinal herbs according to this prescription and take the medicine. You'll be all right.

Qin Yueren began learning medicine.

He climbed mountains to collect herbs.

He learned acupuncture.

Under the guidance of Doctor Changsang, Qin Yueren had mastered all sorts of medical skills and therapies: acupuncture and moxibustion, stone needling, hot medicated compress, massage, surgical operations, decoction of medicinal ingredients. Soon he became known far and wide.

Zhao Jianzi, a great officer of the state of Jin, is critically ill. I was sent here for you to treat him.

He has been unconscious for five days, and hasn't eaten anything.

Although his pulse is weak, he can still be saved. Don't worry, Madam!

He wakes up!

4

Mr. Qin is really a reincarnation of Bian Que!

Bian Que was a legendary magic bird, which could cure people's diseases with its long beak. Since then the magic doctor was known as Bian Que.

Bian Que often came across people believing in sorcery.

Where is the sorcerer? Why hasn't he come yet?

He puts on airs. When we offered him one hundred taels of silver, he didn't even blink.

Give him another hundred taels of silver!

Is there a patient? Let me go in and have a look.

I'm Bian Que. Is your son ill?

My son has offended ghosts and gods. How can you cure his diseases?

Since Bian Que, a famous doctor, is here, you don't need me anymore.

Mr. Sorcerer, it's you whom I invite, not him. Come in please.

The son of the master died that day.

The sorcery of the sorcerer does do great harm to people!

At that time China was divided into many states. Bian Que, together with his pupils, practised medicine throughout the states. One day Bian Que was held up by a person sent by the King of the state of Qin when he was just ready to go out.

The king knows that you are experienced and knowledgeable, so he invites you to go to the imperial palace to chat with him.

Haha! What you have said is interesting! Next time tell me more interesting things you have experienced in other places.

Sure.

To speak frankly, Your Majesty, you have got a disease which is hidden inside your skin, and it should be treated immediately.

Have I got a disease? Inside the skin? Haha! You're making fun of me? Come on, see the doctor off!

Doctors like to consider a healthy person a patient to show off their skills. Bian Que is a man like this!

Your Majesty is in high spirits, carefree and contented. You will live a long life.

A few days later.

Your Majesty, your disease has gone inside you blood vessel. If it is not treated now, it will become even worse.

I'm very well. You may go.

Several days passed.

Your Majesty, your disease has gone inside your internal organs. It'll become very dangerous.

What's the matter? Bian Que turned his head and left as soon as he saw me this morning.

Let me ask him about it.

Why did you go away as soon as you saw the king this morning?

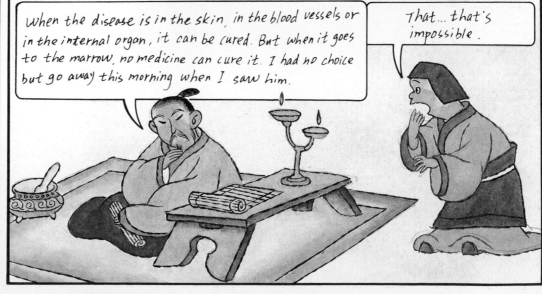

When the disease is in the skin, in the blood vessels or in the internal organ, it can be cured. But when it goes to the marrow, no medicine can cure it. I had no choice but go away this morning when I saw him.

That... that's impossible.

On the way they heard the news of Qi Huanhou's death.

More than ten days later, Bian Que and his pupils arrived in the state of Wei.

9

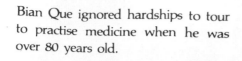

Bian Que ignored hardships to tour to practise medicine when he was over 80 years old.

Doctor Li, lead Bian Que here to see me as soon as he arrives.

Yes, Your Majesty.

What's the matter, Doctor Li?

His Majesty wants to see Bian Que, I'm afraid that I can't be an imperial physician.

It's not a problem. Let's kill him.

Be careful!

That evening.

It's midnight. If you have anything to tell me, please come tomorrow.

A child is going to die! Please save his life, Mr. Bian Que.

Zi Yang, get up quickly and let's see the child.

11

Bian Que was killed. However, he handed down his rich medical experiences to his nine pupils, who followed his principles of practising medicine.

12

The Principles of "Six Persons Not to Treat"

I. Not to treat those who are overbearing and self-indulgent.
II. Not to treat those who care for money more than their health.
III. Not to treat those who cannot take care of themselves.
IV. Not to treat those who have both *yin* and *yang qi* (vital energy).
V. Not to treat those who are thin and weak, and cannot take medicine.
VI. Not to treat those who believe in sorcery but not in medicine.

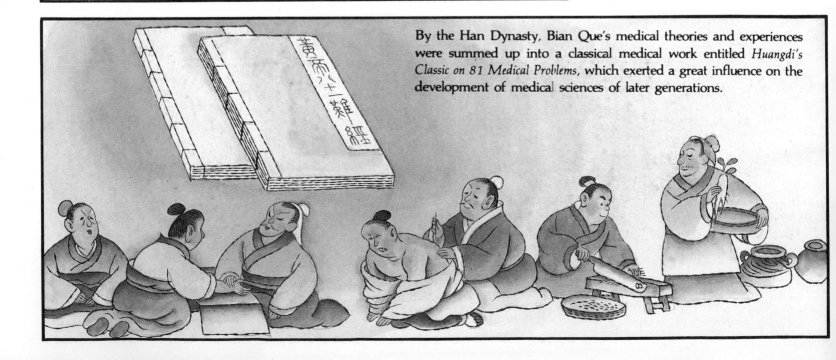

By the Han Dynasty, Bian Que's medical theories and experiences were summed up into a classical medical work entitled *Huangdi's Classic on 81 Medical Problems*, which exerted a great influence on the development of medical sciences of later generations.

HUA TUO

A distinguished doctor of ancient China, Hua Tuo (145-208) made remarkable achievements in the diagnosis of diseases and health care, as well as being the first in the world to do surgical operations of the abdominal cavity using anaesthesia.

Look at General Guan! He is really a hero. He is calmly playing chess and totally at ease although Hua Tuo is scraping his bones with a knife.

General Guan is cured as soon as Hua Tuo has finished working. He is worthy of the title of the Most Famous Doctor.

In the second century, Guan Yu, a famous general of the state of Shu, was wounded on the arm by a poisonous arrow. He invited Hua Tuo to scrape the bones for him to get rid of the venom.

However, most patients were not as brave as Guan Yu. They could not stand the pain.

Let's leave quickly. I'd rather die than be in pain.

Mr., he has become unconscious because of pain.

Get rid of the running sore immediately, clean the wound and dress it with medicine.

If there is a herbal medicine which can make a patient unconscious for a time, it'll relieve great pain in him.

In ancient times, doctors were responsible for collecting, planting and making herbs as well as seeing patients.

15

There is really a sesame-seed cake shop.

Shopkeeper, please give me three bowls of vinegar with mashed garlic.

OK.

16

Dear! He throws up a big roundworm.

You're lucky to have met Hua Tuo. He is a real magic doctor.

Please serve us wine and food. After I'm full, I'll go to thank Doctor Hua Tuo.

All right.

Mr. Hua, I have thrown out a roundworm. I can eat meat now.

Thank you for saving my life.

If you eat clean food in the future, the roundworm won't grow in your stomach any more.

What's the use of collecting datura, Doctor Hua?

He told me that datura has the function of anaesthetic. I don't know if it's true or not.

It's true. There is a group of gansters on the other side of the mountain. They soak datura in alcohol and get the people drunk to steal their property.

Ah!

Ah!

You go and collect datura. The more, the better!

Yes!

Add several more medicinal herbs to detoxify the datura, so the anaesthetic will be safe.

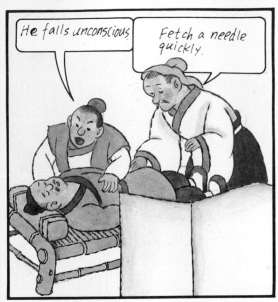

18

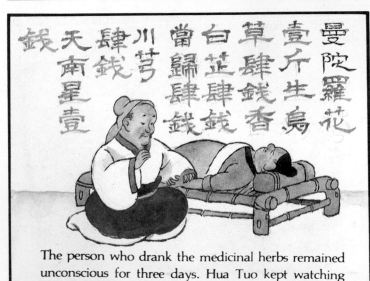

The person who drank the medicinal herbs remained unconscious for three days. Hua Tuo kept watching him all the time.

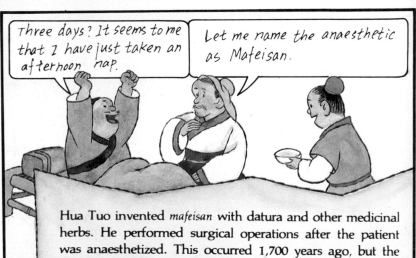

Hua Tuo invented *mafeisan* with datura and other medicinal herbs. He performed surgical operations after the patient was anaesthetized. This occurred 1,700 years ago, but the Western anaesthesia was applied to the patient only less than two hundred years ago.

Why do you write down two different prescriptions for Li Yan and me? We both have headaches.

You caught a cold and should be induced to perspire with drugs. He got dyspepsia caused by improper diet and needs to relieve constipation.

One day Hua Tuo was seeing a patient.

My brother has a stomach ache. Could you please have a look at him?

He has appendicitis. His belly must be cut at once and the appendix removed.

Cut my belly. Dear me!

No.

Ow! I can't bear the pain. Cut my belly quickly!

Give him Mafeisan at once, and get ready for excision.

19

After the patient took mafeisan, Hua Tuo successfully removed appendix.

When he wakes, he will feel his wound is painful. Tell him to take these medicinal herbs on time. He'll be O.K. very soon.

Hua Tuo often went to the mountains to collect medicinal herbs.

Hua Tuo invented the five-animal exercises in imitation of movement of the tiger, deer, bear, ape and eagle. A pupil of Hua Tuo who did the five-animal exercises everyday lived to be over ninety.

Hua Tuo became more and more famous. At the news, Cao Cao, Prime Minister of the state of Wei, sent for Hua Tuo.

22

This was the first sporting activity for building up health in Chinese history. Graceful and relaxed, Hua Tuo's five-animal exercises can build up one's health and invigorate the circulation of blood.

23

I've nothing to do inside the imperial palace. I want to go to the countryside.

As an imperial doctor, how can you serve civilians? You shouldn't go out.

Half a year had passed in the blink of an eye.

We've become birds in a cage.

We may go out under the pretext of collecting medicinal herbs.

Hua Tuo got tired of the imperial life. He returned to his hometown on leave, using the excuse that his wife was sick, and continued to serve the common people.

You are good-for-nothing. You know I've got a headache again. Why not call Hua Tuo back?

Hua Tuo said that his wife was seriously ill and asked to extend his leave.

Hua Tuo left the imperial palace and didn't return. Cao Cao flew into a rage.

Immediately send people to Hua Tuo's home to have a look! If his wife is really ill, give him some gold and silver, and let him stay a few days; if not, escort him to see me!

How bold you are, Hua Tuo. Your wife isn't ill. How dare you cheat the prime minister? Come with us to see Prime Minister at once.

Don't worry my darling. I'll be back soon.

Prime Minister, if you want to be rid of your headache thoroughly, an operation must be done.

Cao Cao got very angry and put Hua Tuo into prison. Hua Tuo meticulously recorded his medical skills and knowledge in prison.

His medical book entitled *Cysticercosis Classic* written on the basis of his many years' experiences disappeared forever.

Wang Weiyi

Born in 987, Wang Weiyi, a Song Dynasty doctor, was the first one to cast models of bronze figures inscribed with the acupuncture channels and points, thus making great contributions to the traditional acupuncture and moxibustion.

Traditional Chinese medicine held that the meridians and collaterals were pathways in which blood and *qi* (vital energy) of the human body were circulated. They formed a network and linked the tissues and organs into an organic whole. If they were impeded, a person would get a disease.

Acupuncture therapy — puncturing a silver needle in a certain location of the meridians, twisting, turning, lifting and inserting the needle to cure the disease by means of clearing the meridians.

Moxibustion therapy — scorching acupoints with lighting moxa.

The unique acupuncture and moxibustion therapy has a history of at least 2,500 years in China.

As early as in 678, Sun Si-mao, a prominent doctor of the Tang Dynasty, drew large and colourful charts of acupuncture and moxibustion, in which twelve regular meridians and eight extra meridians of the body were illustrated.

Since the Tang Dynasty, acupuncture and moxibustion had been listed formally as the official medical education.

I like to listen to Mr. Wang's lecture the most.

Well, his lecture is really good. But I tremble when I think I must puncture myself on a trial basis.

Stop talking. Mr. Wang is coming.

Wang Weiyi drew a teaching model with acupoints and channels that night.

Commissioner, could you please give this to the emperor and ask him to have two bronze figures cast for use in teaching.

Commissioner, what about the suggestion on casting two bronze figures?

The emperor said that people had learned acupuncture according to charts of acupoints since ancient time. It should not be changed.

Commissioner, could you please ask the emperor again?

Let's talk about it later.

The Fourth Lord asks Doctor Wang to see his son.

Lord, Doctor Wang is here.

No problem for your son. He will be O.K. after I puncture him.

He deserves to be called the magical acupuncturist. Come on, award him 20 taels of silver.

I don't want any reward. But could you ask the emperor's permission for casting two bronze figures.

Okay, let me try.

The emperor finally agreed to cast the bronze figures.

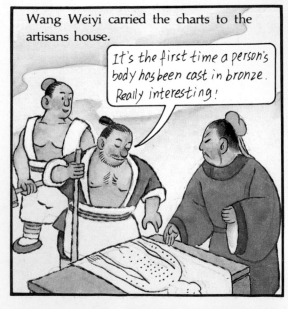

Wang Weiyi carried the charts to the artisans house.

It's the first time a person's body has been cast in bronze. Really interesting!

Can the bronze figures be made hollow? If so, they will be light.

If we put the offal of the animal inside the figure, it will look like a real man! Ha! Ha!

It sounds reasonable.

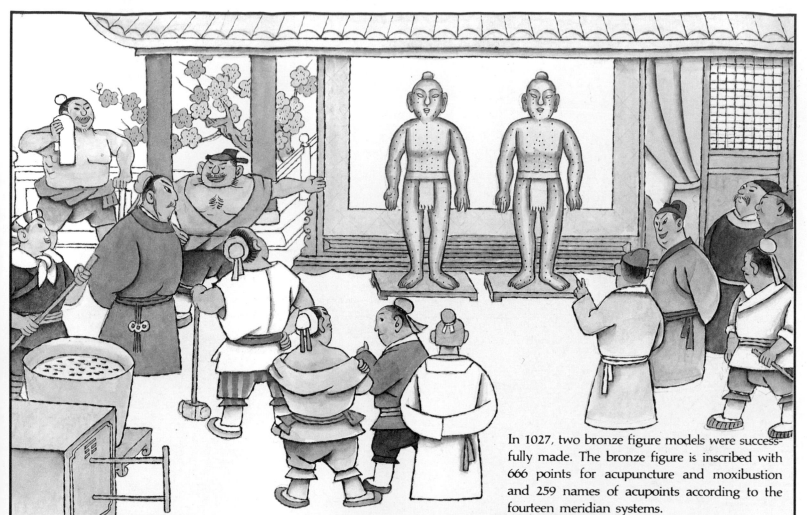

In 1027, two bronze figure models were successfully made. The bronze figure is inscribed with 666 points for acupuncture and moxibustion and 259 names of acupoints according to the fourteen meridian systems.

Emperor Ren Zong came to see the bronze figure.

Since then it has been much more convenient for students in the Imperial Medical Institute to learn acupuncture and moxibustion.

The Imperial Medical Institute introduced a strict examination system in order to train qualified doctors.

In the same year, the *Illustrated Manual of Acupoints* was engraved on a stone tablet so more people could learn about it.

Wang Weiyi summed up acupuncture before the Song Dynasty, and corrected many mistakes. He also wrote a three-volume book entitled *Illustrated Manual of Acupoints on Bronze Figure*, which became a model for acupuncture at that time.

Li Shizhen

Li Shizhen (1518-1593) was a distinguished doctor of the Ming Dynasty. He spent 27 years writing the most complete guide to medicines of ancient China entitled *Compendium of Materia Medica*.

34

Zhang Yan, what's the matter?

Doctor Li, you weren't at home yesterday. My mother took medicine he suggested and died afterwards.

Let me have a look at the prescription.

Here you are.

The prescription isn't wrong. Let's go to your home to see the remaining medicine.

The drug store misused gouwen as huangjing (both Gouwen and huangjing are Chinese herbal medicines). You should go to the drugstore.

This is the drugstore.

Doctor Li, read the descriptions in the book entitled Rihua Materia Medica. It clearly states that gouwen and huangjing are the same herbal medicines.

Storekeeper, read descriptions in this book entitled Materia Medica of the Ming Dynasty. Gouwen is very toxic and huangjing is nonpoisonous. If they are misused, people might be killed.

This...

These two books have two ways of saying the same thing. I shouldn't have been blamed for it.

Both the doctor and the drugstore are in no way to blame, but my mother died wrongly.

Li Shizhen's father was also a doctor. That night Li Shizhen and his parents were enjoying the cool in the courtyard.

Shizhen, are you still thinking about the matter which happened in the morning?

Father, we have a dozen medical books at home, in which many errors can be found. Why can't we write a new one?

You are talking big. Revision of the materia medica is the imperial court's business. How can a folk doctor complete it?

Is doctor Li in?

Mr. Li, I'm from the Palace of King Chu. I come here to invite your so to treat my young master.

Your son has had a fainting attack, but the prescription doesn't suit him.

Which dose of medicine is wrong?

This prescription shouldn't be wrong.

Try this prescription.

Steward, go and make up the prescription of herbal medicine quickly.

He's vomiting. Report to the king quickly.

We have enough superior herbal medicines, but Li Shizhen prescribed some inferior ones. Humph!

He even throw up the gall bladder.

Dad!

The baby's thrown up everything he had in his stomach. He is all right now.

In 1556, Li Shizhen was appointed chief director of the Imperial Medical Institute. Usually he did not have much to do, so he stayed in the House of Longevity Medicine, and the Storehouse of Imperial Medicine, gaining knowledge about all sorts of herbal medicines.

The Imperial Medical Institute also had medical books from all dynasties, which provided Li Shizhen with new insights and strengthened his resolve to revise the materia medica.

Hey, look at this paragraph on badou: A person will die after taking one badou while a mouse will increase its weight by 30 liang (1 liang= 50 grams) after taking one badou. Ha! Ha! It's ridiculous.

Why doesn't the Imperial Medical Institute revise the materia medica?

You know, the emperor believes in sorcery rather than medicine. Doctors in the Imperial Medical Institute all try to make pills for immortality. No one is responsible for the revision of the materia medica.

If nobody is responsible for that, I will be.

Write down—increasing three times of mercury and cinnabar, or the elixirs of life can't be done. The emperor will condemn us.

One day, doctors in the Imperial Medical Institute were discussing official business.

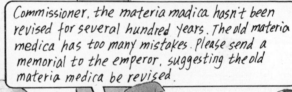

Commissioner, the materia medica hasn't been revised for several hundred years. The old materia medica has too many mistakes. Please send a memorial to the emperor, suggesting the old materia medica be revised.

The Imperial Medical Institute is to serve the emperor. At present, we are short of money to refine the pills of immortality. How can we spend so much effort and money in revising the materia medica?

He is merely a herbalist!

Li Shizhen, it's not enough for you to know only low-class herbal medicines. You may go around the pill-making house and improve your medical skills.

Commissioner, mercury and cinnabar are very poisonous. How can they be made into pills of immortality?

How can you talk so wildly? You vainly attempt to change the ancestors classics and slander the alchemists. Your suggestions can't be authorized.

Li Shizhen was so angry that he resigned from his post using the excuse of sickness and returned to his hometown.

Unexpectedly, Li Shizhen's father had died several months ago.

They're the books your father asked me to transfer to you. He said that you may need them in revising the materia medica.

Father, I have made up my mind to revise the materia medica since the imperial court refuses to revise it.

People from all sides contributed their prescriptions, which greatly inspired Li Shizhen.

At night Li Shizhen checked, arranged and categorized the prescriptions and herbal medicines in accordance with the medical books.

In 1565, Li Shizhen, with innumerable questions about the ancient materia medica, started his ten-year expedition.

Hi, throw down the stem of noble dendrobium, a doctor wants to see it.

Yes.

Pal, do you know the herbal medicine called zhiyuan?

Surely I know it. The small-leaf zhiyuan grows here, and the big-leaf zhiyuan is transported here from other provinces. The two zhiyuans have different medicinal properties.

Write down what he says quickly. The kaibao Materia Medica and the Commentaries on Materia Medica introduce two zhiyuans, which are contradictory.

Ah, the Wudang Moutain is really steep!

They arrived in the Wudang Mountain after several months journey.

43

44

They walked thousands of miles, mastering a lot of information which was needed for the revision of the book. Finally they arrived home.

Li Shizhen divided his medical information gathered into 16 parts and 62 categories according to plant, animal, mineral.... This broke with the method of classification in the past according to the grade of herbal medicines: superior, middle and inferior, and was very close to the contemporary scientific classification principle.

Li Shizhen wrote down in detail the name, producing area, shape, cultivating and collecting method, smell and function of each medicine, and enclosed the shape sketch of each medicine.

After 27 years of hard work, at the age of 61, Li Shizhen finally completed the monumental work entitled the *Compendium of Materia Medica*.

The 52-volume encyclopedia, with 1.9 million characters, contained descriptions of 1,892 medicines, with 1,160 illustrations and 11,096 prescriptions.

In 1596, the *Compendium of Materia Medica* came out, causing a great stir. Bookstores all over the country made copies of the book one after another. It became a great classic work of Chinese medicine. By then, Li Shizhen had been dead for three years. Later, the book reputed as the great medical work in the Orient was translated into many languages.